Edition Schott

Alvin Singleton

b.1940

Fifty Times Around the Sun

for Clarinet and Piano

ED 30087

www.schott-music.com

Mainz · London · Madrid · New York · Paris · Prague · Tokyo · Toronto
© 1999 SCHOTT MUSIC CORPORATION, New York · Printed in USA

Duration: ca. 11 minutes

World Premiere:
July 15, 1999 Portland, OR
Chamber Music Northwest at Reed College

David Shifrin/clarinet
Anne-Marie McDermott/piano

*Dedicated to Paul L. King in honor of his 50th birthday, and commissioned for premiere performance
at Chamber Music Northwest by Clarice G. King, Mary Claire King, Emily King Colwell,
Joseph Ellen, Jessica Dial, Linda Magee, and Craig Fisk.*

FIFTY TIMES AROUND THE SUN

Alvin Singleton
(1999)

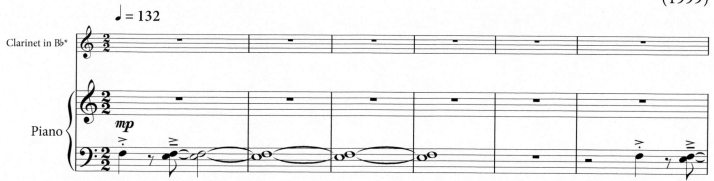

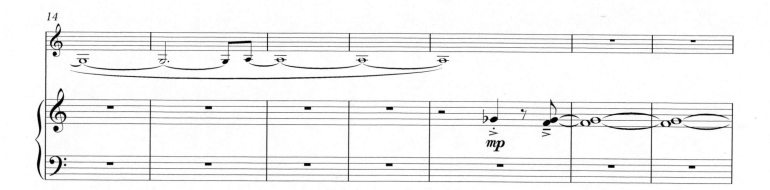

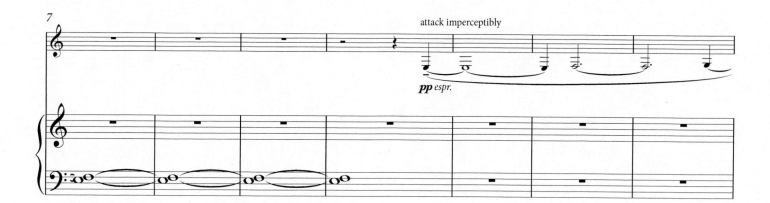

*suono reale

2

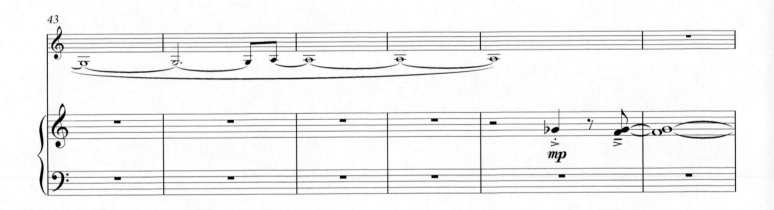

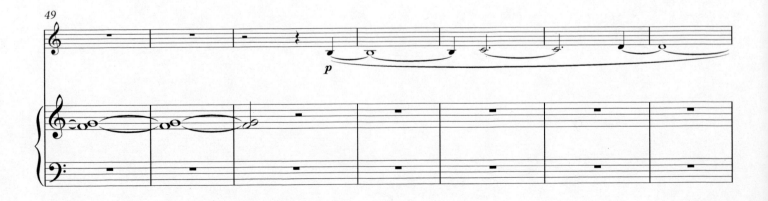

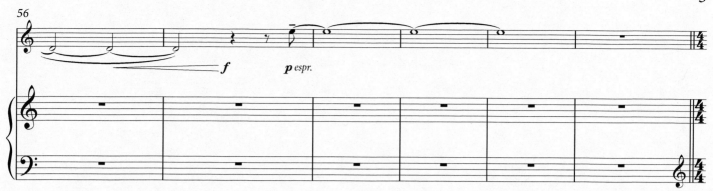

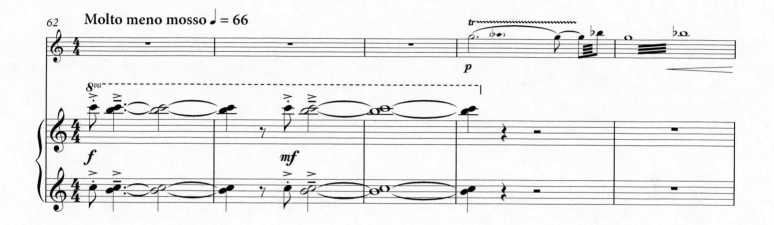

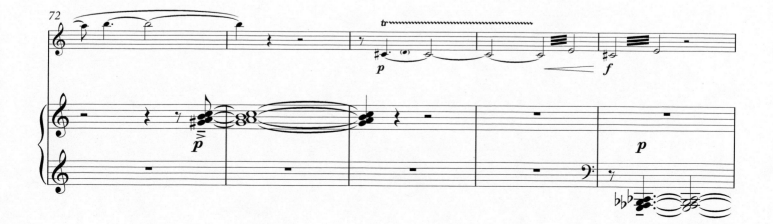

4

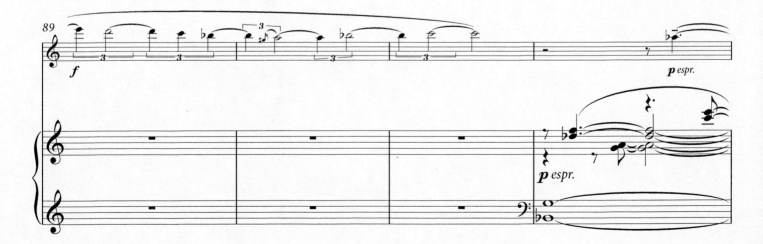

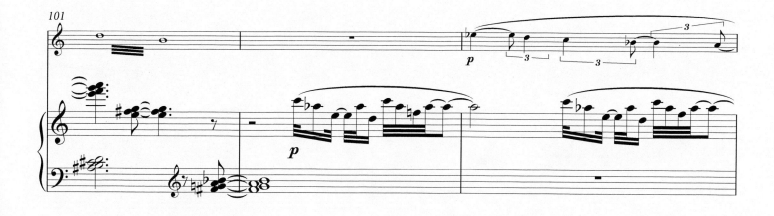

6

Clarinet in B♭

Dedicated to Paul L. King in honor of his 50th birthday, and commissioned for premiere performance at Chamber Music Northwest by Clarice G. King, Mary Claire King, Emily King Colwell, Joseph Ellen, Jessica Dial, Linda Magee, and Craig Fisk.

FIFTY TIMES AROUND THE SUN

Alvin Singleton
(1999)

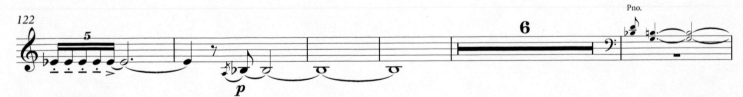

4

Tempo primo ♩ = 132

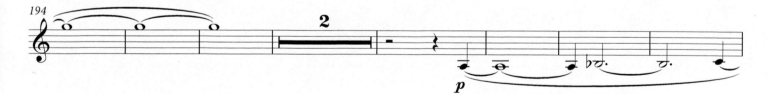

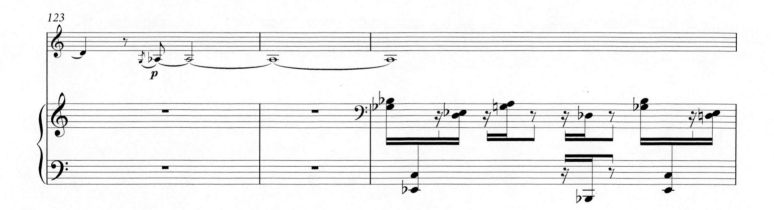

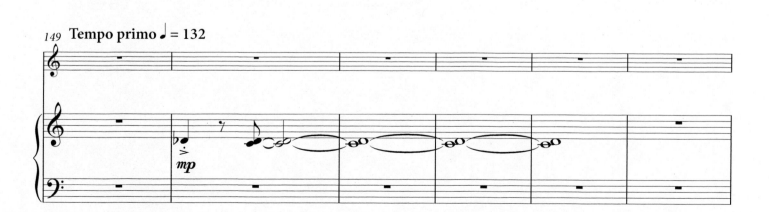

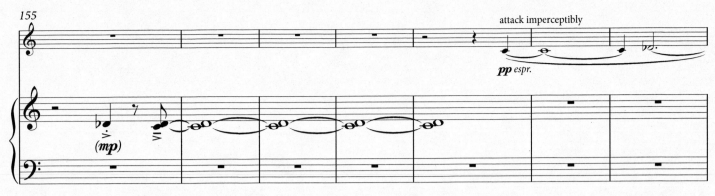

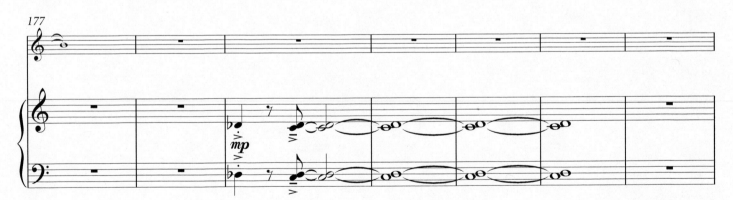

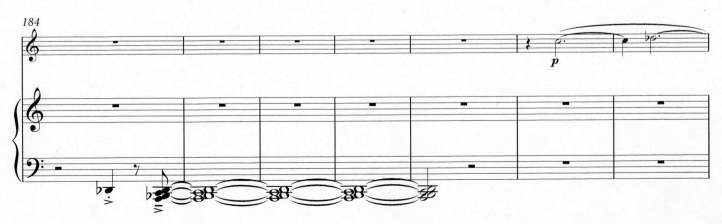

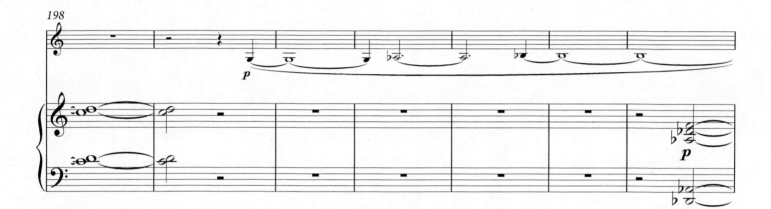

Atlanta. June 3, 1999